The cuckoo in Beijing's nest

The bird's nest is breathtaking, but the steel framework will have produced about 90,000 tonnes of CO_2 in its manufacture.

Shaun McCarthy, Chair, Commission for a Sustainable London 2012

" We have all seen the pictures on the TV and in the papers, but nothing could prepare me for the experience of the Bird's Nest. The stadium is truly breathtaking and the emotional experience of being there to see the world's elite sports people compete is like nothing I have ever witnessed.

I was at Wembley to see my small town football club lift the FA cup in 1976 and I saw England lose to the Germans on penalties in the Euro 96 semi-final; I also saw the England rugby union team win back-to-back Grand Slams at Twickenham, but these do not compare to the sense of excitement and national pride which emanates from every person here and resonates in the very fabric of the building.

London will not compete on these terms, the buildings will not be as iconic and we won't have better fireworks. So what can we learn?

I expect London 2012 to be iconic in its sustainability. When we see the 2012 Olympic flame ignited, it will be fuelled by a form of renewable energy which is still being developed by EDF. This, and many other innovations will show the world what London can do.

The Bird's Nest took 45,000 tonnes of steel to construct. When you witness this mass of steel first hand it becomes obvious that the steel is mostly there to support more steel for decorative purposes.

There are no figures for the amount of concrete used, but London expects to use 1 million tonnes and Beijing could easily double this figure. The science of "Embodied Energy" is relatively new and has only recently begun to be considered in construction. Depending on how the energy was generated, it takes at least 2 tonnes of CO_2 to make a tonne of steel and 4 tonnes to make a tonne of concrete.

According to Greenpeace, the Beijing team has eliminated up to 1.5 million tonnes of CO_2 through energy saving projects, but this figure is likely to be dwarfed by the energy used to create the facilities and infrastructure, which could be the equivalent of the annual emissions of an airline. London 2012 will have lighter, smarter buildings that minimize their impact on the environment in construction and in use.

Shaun McCarthy, 22 August, 2008
Chair, Commission for a Sustainable London 2012
www.cslondon.org
www.actionsustainability.com "

Reusable and Adaptable Wood Structures

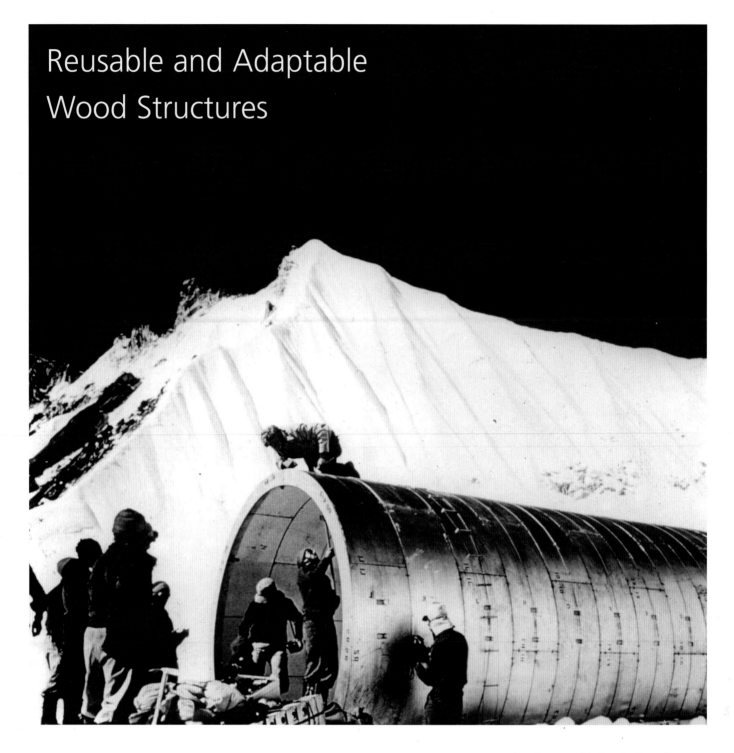

We live in a world that is changing all the time, where flexibility is important, not least in the built environment. Increasingly we need structures that can go up, come down, move, be adapted and rethought, whether for a new classroom to house a sudden influx of children, a ticket booth for a summer attraction, a temporary toilet block, or the whole development of the London Olympics for one brief summer in 2012.

Dr James Milledge, a member of the expedition, wrote:

"The hut was made of boxed-up sections in marine plywood, with no part greater than a porter load. Porters carried it out from Kathmandu to the Khumbu, and Sherpas moved it up to its site. It was very well insulated, and we had no problem keeping it warm with the kerosene stove especially designed for it. It was cylindrical in shape, 7m long by 3m in diameter, and was painted with silver paint."

But we also live in a world where the visual impact of the built environment is important. Where imaginative design and quality materials reflect our cultural values and create a special sense of place. And, above all, we have to find new ways of building that respect the need to preserve our planet for generations to come.

This publication shows how wood is uniquely able to meet these needs. It illustrates how, with imaginative design, wood structures can be reused. In other words, how we can recycle whole structures, not just their constituent parts.

The 'Silver Hut' designed by TRADA for Sir Edmund Hillary's 1960/61 Himalayan expedition is an early example. Made in Britain in 100 pieces, it was transported in kit form to Nepal, carried up a mountain, assembled in four hours and used in sub-zero conditions. It was later dismantled, carried down again, reassembled and used first as a hospital, and then later as a training hut.

Now the 2012 Olympics challenge the UK construction industry to create buildings and infrastructures that are ever more sustainable. Could London's temporary pavilion become Glasgow's art gallery?

The case studies assembled by TRADA and wood for good show how wood's credentials – as the most sustainable mainstream building material we have – can be exploited anywhere that structures need to be relocated, reconfigured and reused.

Why reuse?

Recycling is a cornerstone of sustainable living. Yet when it comes to buildings, we usually demolish and start again from scratch.

It is true that the construction industry is getting better at recovering materials from demolition. But the fact is that the recovery, reprocessing and reconstruction operations consume large amounts of energy and materials that cannot be renewed. How much better it would be to recycle entire structures and save this wasteful reconstitution.

Location
The demand for services and accommodation is constantly changing because of:
• Industry and people moving in response to changing circumstances
• The ageing of the population
• Special events, such as the Olympics, imposing high but short-term demands.

Facilities no longer needed in one area are in acute demand elsewhere – a redundant school building can be relocated to a 'younger' neighbourhood, or stay put and be transformed into a clinic for older residents.

Cost
Materials and sub-assemblies typically account for 40% of the cost of conventional construction; more for structures built off site. If we can reuse entire existing building systems, instead of buying new, the cost savings will be appreciable.

It is normally cheaper to commission a reused structure than a new one, especially where the original designers have thought about demountability. For example, The Globe at CERN (page 15) demonstrates a 25% saving. The cost of the original Palais de L'Equilibre was 10 million Swiss francs in 2002, whereas its reconstruction in 2004 cost just 7.5 million Swiss francs, which included

the sound proofing, insulation and heating systems not required for the temporary Expo 2002 building.

Indeed, as the appetite for reusing buildings increases, buildings designed to be demountable will acquire a residual value that can be accounted for in life cycle analysis and property values.

Speed
Taking into account the entire procurement programme, a reused structure will normally be quicker to realise.

A new structure:

Procure materials	Manufacture and sub-assemble	Install on site

A reused structure:

Disassemble	Relocate	Install on site

Why wood?

A sustainable European supply

Although deforestation is a problem in global terms, it is not a major issue in Europe. Europe's forests are increasing by 661,000 hectares per year[1], thanks to effectively implemented legislation requiring forest owners to replace harvested trees.

The Food and Agriculture Organization of the United Nations notes that "net increases in the extent of forest, in forest plantations and in growing stock are positive trends towards sustainable forest management in the region. All indications are that European countries have successfully stabilized or increased their forest areas…"

The European construction industry sources the great majority of its timber from Europe's forests, importing just 3% of its softwood and 16% of its hardwood consumption from outside Europe.[2]

Responsible sourcing

Chain of Custody certified wood provides additional reassurance of its legality and sustainability. The use of certified wood can lead to an improved rating level in the Code for Sustainable Homes.[3] Good supplies of PEFC and FSC Chain of Custody softwood are available.[4]

When specifying hardwood, particularly tropical species, it is essential to insist on credible Chain of Custody or Verified Progress certification. For further advice, ask your specialist merchant. The use of responsibly sourced tropical hardwoods may help conserve tropical forests since it helps provide a long-term economic return on this land area.

No other mainstream construction material has such an effective system to ensure responsible sourcing.

Workability and adaptability

Wood is light and easy to handle on and off site. It is also easier to cut, drill and shape than concrete and metal. The factory processes are simpler and demand less energy than steel-framed fabrication.

Strength to weight

Wood is light and strong. An equivalent steel beam is typically 20% heavier than an equivalent timber glulam beam and a concrete beam is six times the weight.

Low weight reduces groundworks. Foundations can be smaller and even temporary: for example, screw piles that can be extracted when the structure is moved away.

Thermal performance

Wood is a good thermal insulator. The thermal conductivity of softwood timber is typically some 6 times lower than brickwork or heavyweight concrete block, over 8 times lower than concrete, almost 400 times lower than steel and over a thousand times lower than aluminium.[5]

Aesthetic appeal

Engineered wood products combine structural and decorative finishes, and produce lightweight, airtight structures. Wood structures offer stunning visual solutions that can be complemented by the natural beauty and warmth of wood claddings and linings.

Recycling and reuse

To make the most of the carbon benefit of using wood products, they should be used for as long as possible. Good design detail and effective maintenance are important, but when a building reaches the end of its life, timber elements can often be reused.

The length of time over which carbon is stored can also be prolonged by recycling. Unlike concrete and steel, wood requires very little reprocessing before it is reused, and recycled wood finds a ready market in the panel products sector, as well as in emerging applications like animal bedding.

Increasingly, end-of-life wood is being chipped or converted into pellets as the ultimate biomass fuel. This trend is set to continue as pressure from the EU Landfill Directive makes landfill progressively more expensive.[6]

Wood is 'low carbon'

Using wood from sustainably managed forests is one of the best ways to reduce a building's carbon footprint. Preparing wood for construction results in far lower CO_2 emissions than other construction materials. The Edinburgh Centre for Carbon Management estimates that between 0.7 and 1.1 tonnes of carbon dioxide is saved for every cubic metre of wood used instead of other building materials.

The more wood you use, the nearer you get to being carbon neutral. But it gets better! Buildings made with solid wood panels (SWP) in walls, floors and roofs are likely to have a negative carbon footprint. In other words, the carbon absorbed as the trees grow exceeds the carbon consumed in the other construction materials of the building, not just that consumed with the harvesting, drying, machining and transport of the timber.

For example, the White Design and Wilmott Dixon Re-thinking School project at BRE's innovation park used SWP to achieve a negative carbon footprint, with the wood saving 40.9 tonnes of carbon dioxide during the materials' lives from cradle to site.[7]

Comparing equivalent glulam, steel and concrete beams, the energy needed to produce a 305mm x 165mm steel beam is six times that of a 550mm x 135mm softwood glulam beam. And a 400mm x 250mm reinforced concrete beam requires five times as much energy.[8] Most of the UK's energy is produced from fossil fuels at present. Hence, reducing energy consumption will reduce CO_2 emissions. Wood construction reduces a building's carbon footprint, encourages afforestation, increases carbon storage and demonstrates a clear environmental contribution and commitment.

Captured carbon

The potential impact of wood's capacity to 'lock away' carbon is not widely understood. Reused wood structures lengthen the beneficial impact of wood by extending the time carbon is locked away. The carbon cycle diagram contrasts wood and other mainstream materials such as concrete, steel and masonry.

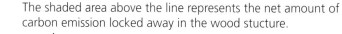

The shaded area above the line represents the net amount of carbon emission locked away in the wood stucture.

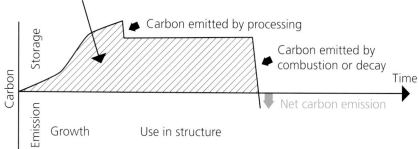

Carbon cycle for wood structures
The net amount of carbon locked away is reduced by process energy and finally by decay or burning in a biomass energy system at the end of its life cycle.

This ignores transport and reprocessing energy at the end of life.

Carbon cycle for reused wood structures
Note how the second use of a wood structure increases the time that carbon is safely locked away in the wood.

The shaded area below the line represents the net amount of carbon emitted by the structure.

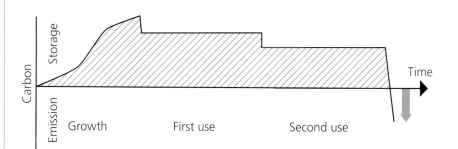

Carbon cycle for other materials
Other materials do not absorb any carbon. And in most cases, the amount of energy needed for the extraction, processing and construction processes far exceeds what is needed for an equivalent wood structure. That is why other materials end their life cycle with a greater emission of carbon.

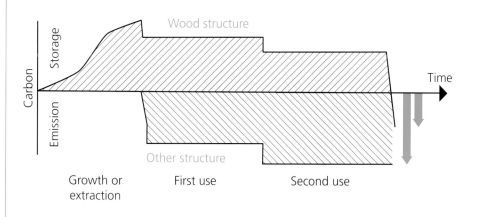

Combining these diagrams shows the net advantage of wood even more dramatically.

Structures for major events

Major events, such as exhibitions, sporting competitions and mass entertainments, call for a wide range of structures from large stadiums and pavilions to small kiosks and offices.

Planners of major events are responding to increasing public aspirations for sustainability. For example, the organisers of London's 2012 Olympics say: "We want London 2012 to be the first 'sustainable' Games, setting new standards for major events." Heading their list of five key areas is combating climate change, followed by reducing waste, enhancing biodiversity, promoting inclusion and improving healthy living.

While the choice of materials has a direct impact on climate change and waste, the way materials are produced and used also affects biodiversity, inclusion and healthy living.

In combating climate change, designers can take advantage of wood's special feature that sets it apart from other construction materials – its uniquely low carbon footprint.

Reducing waste means much more than recycling off cuts. As well as eliminating waste from construction processes, we need to be reusing and adapting whole structures. The case studies in this publication illustrate how, with the right considerations from the outset, structures can be adapted, relocated and reused, and that these principles can be readily applied to entire wood buildings.

The companion to this publication, *Wide-Span Wood Sports Structures*, (available free as a pdf download from the publications section of www.woodforgood.com or the technical information library section of www.trada.co.uk. A limited number of copies available from wood for good) illustrates the versatility of wood structures for sports facilities. These are typical of the structures needed for major events.

Via nineteen detailed case studies, it shows how wood – the most sustainable of all building materials – can deliver major event facilities of exceptional, world-class standard.

Sections include:
• Structural materials
• Structural forms
• Structural elements
• Connections.

Reusable wood structures

By 'reusing' whole structures, we mean using them again when they are no longer needed for their original purpose. For example, an Olympics office that is dismantled, transported, and then reassembled elsewhere for use as a school – known as a 'legacy' use.

Adaptability exists when:
- A building can be altered internally for change of use. For example, demountable partitions enable a classroom block to be converted into a medical centre
- A building can be disassembled and re-erected in a new form. For example, a rectangular modular system house is converted into a tee-form office.

The case studies in this book are colour keyed to show how entire wood structures can be reused in four ways:

Mobile structures
the whole structure can be picked up and relocated

Intentionally demountable structures
intended to be pulled apart and reassembled

Potentially demountable structures
potential to be pulled apart and reassembled

Adaptable for change of use
the layout can be readily adapted

THE WORLD'S SMALLEST CINEMA
It is hard to imagine a reusable building less complicated than this enchanting mobile cinema. There is no taking apart and making good. Just charge the batteries, hitch it up and tow it to the next location.

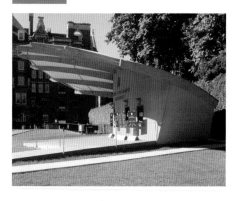

WESTMINSTER TICKET OFFICE
This ticket office for summer visitors to the Westminster Houses of Parliament had to be capable of being dismantled and stored in a flat pack form ready for re-erection the following year.

ECOCANOPY
Introduced to the education sector in 2007, EcoCanopy has the lifespan and robustness of a permanent building but is equally at home as a temporary solution. The bonus is that EcoCanopy can be demounted and reused elsewhere.

CLIENT — Royal Collection Enterprises

ARCHITECTS — Hopkins Architects

STRUCTURAL ENGINEER — Arup

CONTRACTOR — Holloway White Allom

JOINERY CONSULTANT AND TIMBER SUPPLIER — Cheeseman Interiors

Buckingham Palace Ticket Office
Green Park, London, 1995

OVERVIEW

Erected at the edge of Green Park every summer from 1995 until recently, the ticket office welcomed some 250,000 visitors for the public opening of Buckingham Palace. The combination of warm red cedar, spruce struts and white fabric complemented the summery feel of this corner of The Royal Park. The cabin is detailed and built like a boat, and can be transported on a lorry and bolted together on arrival. Built for £100,000 in 1995, the ticket office was dismantled annually for winter storage. The structure is currently awaiting a new use.

Hopkins Architects' creation takes its gently curving geometry from the radius of the nearby monument to Queen Victoria, and its orientation ensured that visitors could look towards their goal as they queued for tickets. The ticket office uses timber from renewable sources, is naturally ventilated, and had minimal impact on this important site.

The 15 metre long ticket office with its six teller positions is contained within a secure 50m² timber enclosure. The cabin, made from varnished cedar strip fixed to timber studding, forms a 'hull' shell. Prefabricated in two parts, it was brought to site on its integral wheels, bolted together, then levelled and anchored on retractable jacks.

A structure of 25mm birch-faced plywood ribs set at 750 centres and bolted to a steel chassis makes up a hooped frame. The ribs are exposed internally. External 65mm x 18mm thick Western red cedar strips stiffen the structure. At each corner, the strips run vertically and are resolved in a quadrant at head and base, enclosing the eaves corners and giving a totally smooth and flush finish. Yacht varnish (not normally recommended for timber buildings) applied internally and externally enhance the rich colour of the timber. The monocoque cabin provides the horizontal stability.

Surrounding the cabin is a modular timber deck, supported on adjustable feet, with roped rail and balustrade along the edge. The laminated spruce masts connect to a head boss at either end of the cabin. They are linked above the membrane by a catenary cable that picks up the fabric from above via flitched 'coat hangers'; these give the roof the profiled appearance and necessary structural curvature.

The canopy consists of a single piece of white translucent and lightweight modacrylic fabric, as used in sail making. It is approximately 24m long by 7m wide and, at its highest, 5.5m above the deck. The fabric canopy is held in position by laminated spruce masts and spars with stainless steel nautical fittings. A system of cables attached to ground anchor points stabilizes and tensions the structure.

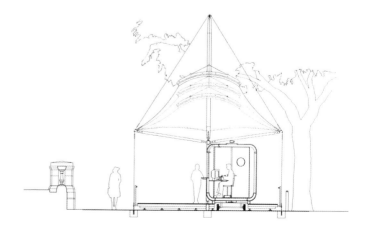

FIRST CLIENT (2002)	The Swiss Confederation
SECOND CLIENT (2004-2006)	CERN
ARCHITECT	Groupe-H: Herve Dessimoz
STRUCTURAL ENGINEER	Timber specialist Charpente-Concept: Thomas Buchi
TIMBER SUPPLIER	Ducret-Orges
CONTRACTOR (2002)	A consortium including Holzloft, Gaille, Ducret-Orges, Mosimann, Tschappat and Boss
CONTRACTOR (2004-2006)	CIB and the Swiss Army

The Globe at Cern
Geneva, Switzerland, 2006

OVERVIEW

It is the tallest structure of its type in the world, about the size of the dome of Saint Peter's Basilica in Rome. Yet, despite its great size, this timber structure was always intended to be relocated.

Much of the timber was used originally in Switzerland's pavilion at the Hanover Expo 2000, and then recycled in Le Palais de l'Equilibre for the Swiss Expo 2002 at Neuchâtel. Designed to be dismantled, it was the only building reused from Expo 2002. In 2004, CERN had it taken from storage and transported some 120km to its site in Geneva where it was reconstructed and opened in 2006 as The Globe of Science and Innovation.

The European Organization for Nuclear Research (CERN, in Geneva) is the world's largest particle physics laboratory. Like the last pieces of a giant jigsaw puzzle, in 2008 CERN switches on the greatest physics experiment ever undertaken, the Large Hadron Collider.

A focal point for welcoming the public, The Globe is a venue for film showings, conferences, exhibitions and debates, and is the departure point for more than 25,000 visitors visiting CERN each year. The Globe is a sphere, 40m in diameter, 27m tall and made entirely of wood; it represents the Earth's future by combining science with innovation. Its structure is reminiscent of the shape of the planet,

while it is made of the most environmentally-friendly of all building materials, wood. The outer shell, resembling a finely spun cocoon, is designed to protect the building from the sun and the elements, just like the Earth's atmosphere. The inner ball, whose frame (like the outer shell) consists of 18 glue-laminated cylindrical arcs of 600mm diameter, is covered with wooden panels. Two spiral pedestrian ramps wind their way up between the outer and inner shells.

Each arc is made of two elements bolted together. Assembly depended on a revolutionary technology to splice the arcs and join them to the gigantic central vortex. This process (resin composed of threaded metal stems sealed using the Ferwood® process) facilitates simple, discreet and economic ways to make rigid, semi-rigid or articulated connections in timber frames.

Five species of timber were used in the Globe's construction – Scots pine, Douglas fir, spruce, larch and Canadian maple – all grown locally. The Swiss forests produce about 700m³ of timber per hour; hence, the 2,500m³ of timber in the structure

represents only about three hour's production.

This is a significant carbon store for as long as the timber is preserved. The trees absorbed 2,500 tonnes of CO_2 and released 1,825 tonnes of oxygen (O_2) during their lifetime.

The timber is emphasised during the day, while at night the Globe is a ball of light. A showcase for the talents of Swiss carpenters, the Globe has taken timber construction to a new level.

CLIENT	Parliamentary Works Service Directorate
ARCHITECTS	Pringle Richards Sharratt Architects
STRUCTURAL ENGINEER	Alan Baxter and Associates with timber specialists Finnforest and Eurban
TIMBER SUPPLIER	Finnforest

Westminster Ticket Office
London, 2003

OVERVIEW

This ticket office for summer visitors to the Westminster Houses of Parliament had to be capable of being dismantled and stored in a flat pack form ready for re-erection the following year. The architect selected a solid wood panel system (SWP) because this lent itself to rapid and repeat assembly, had a low embodied energy and met the tight budget. Not to mention the stunning appearance.

The budget in 2003 for the structure was just £55,000. Having "stressed the need for any facility here to be of the highest quality," English Heritage welcomed the scheme, saying: "The proposals now before us fulfil this criterion entirely." It was used for four summers from 2003, until an alternative solution was found within the Palace of Westminster, and then sold to a Bavarian sports club in 2006.

The 48m² pavilion had four ticket points for customers sheltered under a fabric roof. The form of the building was like a scallop shell with a membrane roof supported on ribs cantilevered from the load bearing walls. The office was naturally ventilated with grilles in the floor and roof cavity.

The walls and roof were Lenotec SWP (81mm thick laminated spruce), which provided a secure enclosure for cashiers and good acoustic and thermal insulation. The translucent PVC-coated polyester roof membrane covered the public area and provided a ventilated cavity above timber panels in the office. The cover was supported on slender beams made from Kerto laminated veneer lumber (LVL) spruce.

The deck was non-slip Thermowood®, which is heat-treated and rot-resistant when in contact with moisture and the ground.

Timbers were harvested from Finnish and Bavarian forests, with Chain of Custody certificates all the way from the forest to the gate of the production facility. CAD/CAM techniques greatly speeded up the translation of a complicated geometry into the finished product through numerically controlled cutting machines in the German factory.

The timber panels were sized for transport by road. The connections were all bolted to allow assembly and dismantling – either timber lap joints for panel-to-panel connections, or galvanised steel brackets for beams and connections to foundations. Some galvanised steel tubes were used as struts for the membrane roof.

Concrete foundation blocks were installed and kept in place for the annual anchoring of the structure via fixing bolts. The structure was transported from Germany and then erected in only three days, just nine weeks after receiving the order.

Monkey Puzzle Pavilion
Six Cities Design Festival, Aberdeen, 2007

CLIENT   The Scottish Executive in collaboration with
                           the Lighthouse Gallery Glasgow, The Robert
                           Gordon University and Aberdeen City Council

ARCHITECTS   Jonathan Woolf Architects

STRUCTURAL ENGINEER   Built Engineers

CONTRACTOR   H & K Joinery

OVERVIEW

This evocative wood pavilion was the centre point in Aberdeen of the Scotland-wide Six Cities Design Festival, providing a focus for information and events. Although designed primarily for its immediate purpose, the prefabricated structure was intended to be demounted and transported to a new site where it could be re-erected, weatherproofed and insulated for long-term use. After the festival, a local sculptor acquired the pavilion for reuse as a studio.

Made entirely from wood, this prefabricated public building was positioned in the main square of the city, its oriented strand timber board (OSB) cladding in bold contrast to the sombre stone surroundings.

The shape of the building created distinct spaces both internally and externally around a central gathering hall for talks, films and children's events, with its four way 'alley' interior layout evoking the scale of a medieval street pattern. The 70m² floor area was capped by a slanted roof forming interior heights from 3.0 – 4.8m.

The brief called for a lightweight sustainable structure that would be easy to erect (in one week) and dismantle; easily transportable, cost-efficient and aesthetically appropriate. The OSB cladding was used to provide a continuous surface and a sculptural effect, as though hewn from a single material. The OSB had a rich 'fossilised' pattern, clearly recognizable as being from nature even though it is industrial. The wall, ceiling and stone floor presented a 'landscape' where the materials, though cut by man, retained their essential substance, evoking both woodland and crag.

The walls were lines of pre-fabricated OSB-clad timber framed panels, each generally 1.2m long and up to 4.8m with the top edge angled to allow for roof fall. The cladding sheets were staggered, screwed and glued to the frames on the internal faces; then all the panels were numbered and transported to site where they were coach-bolted together. Anchorage to the ground was via 120 off-the-peg concrete blocks placed in the bases of panels, in conjunction with purpose-made, precast concrete ground rails. Finally, the exterior cladding was applied and left unpainted.

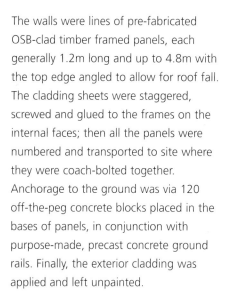

The roof used similar OSB-clad frames supported on pre-fabricated timber I joists with softwood flanges and OSB webbing. The sloping roof offered short-term weather protection with two coats of silicon spray and mastic sealed joints. For the art studio conversion, there will be timber shingle cladding, cavity insulation and a lightweight metal seam bonded roof.

The panels had to be positioned without lifting gear. This was achieved by limiting panel weight to 100kg so that they could be lifted and positioned by four people.

CLIENT Serpentine Gallery

ARCHITECTS Alvaro Siza and Eduardo Souto de Moura

STRUCTURAL ENGINEER Arup

TIMBER SUPPLIER AND CONTRACTOR Finnforest

Serpentine Gallery
Kensington Gardens, London, 2005

OVERVIEW

Each year the Serpentine Gallery commissions an internationally acclaimed architect who has not yet had a building completed in the UK to create a demountable temporary pavilion next to its permanent exhibition in Kensington Gardens. An ambitious design is called for, to be executed at break-neck speed. When opened, less than five months after conception, it was clear that Alvaro Siza's "giant insect, ready to leap" had completely fulfilled the brief. A reusable structure that sat so lightly for one summer, and was then dismantled with such ease, was certainly an achievement.

The Financial Times' architectural correspondent wrote: "This is how architecture should be exhibited and remembered. See it, and Siza's exquisite space will stay with you."

With its 400m² footprint and 17m span, the 2005 Pavilion was larger than previous incarnations. The column-free roof and walls were formed by an undulating offset grid of laminated veneer lumber (LVL) frames. Arup's Advanced Geometry Unit modelled the complex form.

The pavilion was clad externally with 248 transparent polycarbonate panels that each incorporated a solar-powered light. In the evenings, the ethereal pavilion seemed to float over the park just as imagined in the creators' original vision.

The architects' preference for timber inspired Arup's timber specialist Andrew Lawrence to suggest the 'lamella' (thin grid) system. Others had successfully produced regular grid lamella structures; the Serpentine Pavilion was the first to achieve an irregular grid and was unusual

because it works in bending, compared with the original lamellas that worked as arches. The lamella design also avoided the need to bring heavy cranes into the Royal Park.

The structure, designed to Eurocode 5, comprised 427 unique interlocking timber beams in a shifting rhythm, far removed from the static nature of normal grillage structures. Each element was unique, having a different length and inclination. The mortice and tenon connections were a distinctive feature of the 3D 'jigsaw' building that enabled it to be assembled and demounted rapidly. But there

was a concern that disproportionate collapse was possible, through a 'domino' effect, if one node or support were to fail. For this reason alone, the engineers introduced steel bolts at the nodes to provide robustness.

With so many different elements, a sheet material such as Kerto Q laminated veneer lumber (LVL spruce) was the ideal choice, because it could be cut to the shape required. Also, the high shear strength of the Kerto Q would resist the shear forces on the tenons arising from the bending action.

The bases of the LVL wall portals were designed as fixed connections, using exposed surface-fixed plates and screws. Even though this was a temporary structure, the end-grain of the stanchion bases was kept well above the paving to prevent water ingress.

The prefabrication was total and, when the small lightweight elements were transported to site, everything fitted perfectly without adjustment. Another special feature was the complete avoidance of printed drawings and the integrated CAD and CAM. Each of the 427 different elements had 36 co-ordinates to define its shape and fit. The geometries of the 427 elements were defined digitally, which allowed direct communication between Arup and the CNC programmers at Finnforest via spreadsheets.

After the exhibition, the pavilion was sold to a private buyer.

CLIENT	Agentur Milla & Partner, Stuttgart
ARCHITECTS	Gasser/Wittmer, Stuttgart
STRUCTURAL ENGINEER	Finnforest Merk GmbH
TIMBER SUPPLIER	Finnforest Merk GmbH

OVERVIEW

Lenotec solid wood panels (SWP) featured in these 7m-high prefabricated modular pavilions. Designed from scratch by a specialist in demountable structures, the pavilions were just bolted and braced together. What went up simply came down again in reverse order.

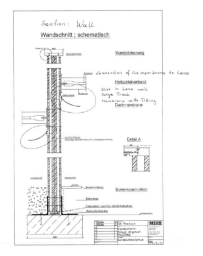

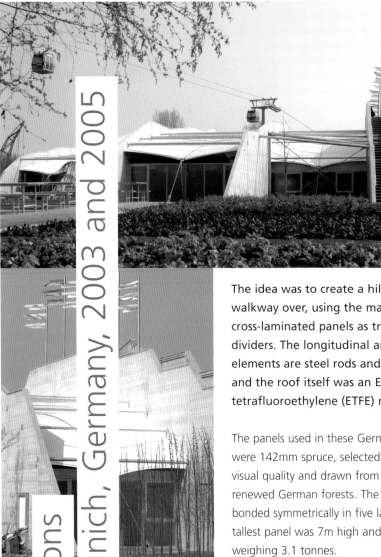

Deutscher Pavilions
Rostock and Munich, Germany, 2003 and 2005

The idea was to create a hill with a walkway over, using the massive cross-laminated panels as transverse dividers. The longitudinal and bracing elements are steel rods and tubes, and the roof itself was an Ethylene tetrafluoroethylene (ETFE) membrane.

The panels used in these German pavilions were 142mm spruce, selected for their visual quality and drawn from constantly renewed German forests. The spruce was bonded symmetrically in five layers. The tallest panel was 7m high and 4.5m wide, weighing 3.1 tonnes.

The footprint of the building was roughly 960m^2, some 60m long and between 12m and 18m across. The whole installation took just 10 weeks.

The Green Spec recognises SWP for its above average performance in reducing global warming and solid waste.[9] Available in thicknesses from 50 to 300mm, panels can be up to 4.8m wide and an astonishing 20m long. Transportation is usually the limiting factor.

Long-lasting Lenotec offers:
- Rapid assembly
- Prefabricated dimensional accuracy and accommodation for building services
- High CO$_2$ storage capacity
- Construction that is vapour permeable
- Pleasant, warm living conditions due to solid, moisture-regulating building components
- Up to 15% more living area compared to alternative types of construction due to its slim construction
- High levels of thermal insulation, air tightness and sound proofing
- Fire resistance up to 90 minutes depending on thickness.

The wood is sourced from sustainable sources and factory waste is used for biomass heating.

The spruce boards are dried in a factory then cross-laminated to produce panels that are dimensionally stable and resistant to warping. The ease of creating large spaces quickly makes cross-laminated products economical as standardized board for ceilings, roofing or walls, or as precisely pre-fabricated, ready-to-fit kits for entire buildings.

CLIENT	The London Borough of Camden
DESIGNER	Cameron Scott
STRUCTURAL ENGINEER	Andrew Smith Consulting Engineers
TIMBER SUPPLIER AND CONTRACTOR	The Timber Frame Company

OVERVIEW

Most of the ingredients for a demountable building are already in place in this open-plan restaurant. The connections are either traditional mortice and tenon joints or bespoke stainless steel connections, and could be dismantled easily without damage. Improvements to ensure an easy relocation would be in the details: roof build up, covering above the windows, choice of fixings and panelised internal finishes.

Terrace Restaurant
Lincoln's Inn Fields, London, 2005

When the London Borough of Camden went shopping for a 120-seat restaurant, their purchase of a timber structure raised local eyebrows. Yet the machined modular timber solution proved to be both economical and environmentally-friendly. And it is still raising eyebrows because of its understated good looks – what the designer modestly calls "simple and honest".

Eliminating internal braces affords the restaurant maximum internal flexibility. The post and beam frame is arranged with a horizontal truss combining top plates, tie beams and stainless steel diagonals to transmit lateral forces to be resolved in the end walls. This produces an uninterrupted internal space of 29m x 7.2m with a spacious apex height of 4.7m. The restaurant seats 120 comfortably with room for another 70 on the deck.

The design had to suit off-site fabrication, maximise on-site efficiency and use sustainable materials. British timbers are Douglas fir (C24) for the primary structure, Sitka spruce for the secondary structure and larch cladding. The panels, sheathing and joinery are of European origin.

The substructure is naturally durable Greenheart hardwood, salvaged from London docks, sitting on compacted crushed (recycled) concrete. A repeat design would probably use local oak instead.

The primary structure was pre-cut in the workshop, test-assembled and then delivered as a kit of parts. The substructure was also prefabricated with a degree of adjustment in order to establish dimensional tolerance for the platform. The secondary structure, including floor, walls and roof, is a bespoke panel system made without specialist equipment. The building was designed using a 3D modelling package that 'built' the restaurant in virtual space. The outcome was that all the systems went together on site without error, and without any computer numerical control of the manufacture.

Rolling steel screens secure the glazed walls at night. These screens are 'stored' at the service end of the building during the day giving a distinctive elevation detail.

Swoosh
Architectural Association, London, 2008

CLIENT	The Architectural Association
ARCHITECTS	Students of AA Intermediate Unit 2, concept by Valeria Garcia
STRUCTURAL ENGINEER	Arup
CONSTRUCTOR	Intermediate Unit 2 students at Hooke Park, Dorset
TIMBER SUPPLIER	Finnforest

OVERVIEW

The Architectural Association's (AA) 2008 Summer Pavilion is an arched structure of interlocking columns and beams cut from Kerto laminated veneer lumber (LVL). The pavilion is an annual project for architectural students to learn about the design, fabrication and assembly of structures that rely on the traditional woodworking crafts.

AA students, together with their tutors, conceived, designed, documented and constructed the pavilion over an academic year. At the end of the summer it was dismantled and moved from Bedford Square to a permanent location. The programme is in its fifth year, and the 2008 pavilion was sponsored by Finnforest, Arup, HOK and Building Design.

The brief was for a demountable summer pavilion with an area of 100m². Adaptability and demountability were an inherent part of the design competition between groups of students.

Hooke Park in Dorset offered the AA a complete timber fabrication workshop

including computer numerical controlled (CNC) machining capability and living accommodation. Here the students learned the crafts of the carpenter and joiner, skills the AA considers are not well understood by architects. The project used timber because it is an environmentally sustainable material. It also afforded a better opportunity both to conceive and implement architectural solutions than other construction materials. The 154m² x 4.5m high pavilion was constructed as an arched column and beam structure. The columns were generated from partial circles. There are eight complete arches in the centre of the pavilion, creating an intimate inner space. The arches gradually rise from the ground to become cantilevers.

The 62 columns (some divided into segments) and the 609 beam elements were cut using a CNC machine, and then hand finished to suit each element's location. Columns were cut out of 51mm thick Kerto and the transverse elements from 29mm Kerto. The components were small enough to be transported by truck for assembly on site. Simple bolted connections with tooth plate connectors were used to allow easy disassembly.

The pavilion rests on two three-tonne steel bases, fabricated off site and bolted together in situ. There is a flitch plate connection between the columns and steel base, and where the columns are spliced.

A 'T' shaped connector is used to join beams to columns. Transverse beams have a bolt into their end grain, which is screwed into a machined pocket in the side of the beam.

The geometry of the pavilion is radially symmetrical but the height varies continuously. As the pavilion elements are all vertical, the shadow reflects the plan onto the ground. This effect changes dramatically throughout the day, adding to the visual experience.

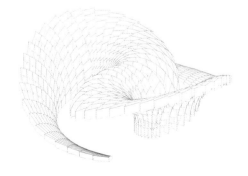

CLIENT	Education sector
ARCHITECTS	Bryden Wood Associates
STRUCTURAL ENGINEER	Alan Baxter Associates
CONTRACTOR	Bailey

OVERVIEW

By any measure of sustainability, EcoCanopy ticks the boxes. Environmentally, the process is low waste, the timber material has low embodied energy and the buildings make meagre demands for heat and light. Economically, it is attractive with lean thinking at every step from manufacture to commissioning. And it delivers durable small-scale buildings ideal for supplying the local education, leisure, healthcare and retail services needed to sustain communities.

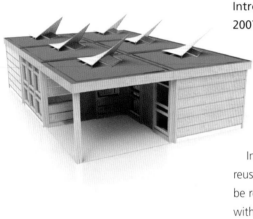

EcoCanopy
Various education sites

Introduced to the education sector in 2007, EcoCanopy has the lifespan and robustness of a permanent building but is equally at home as a temporary solution. The bonus is that EcoCanopy can be demounted and reused.

In fact, 85% of the building can be reused; for example, the wall panels can be reused in any combination, together with the roof canopy. Even the waffle slab can be removed and reused, and the heating and electrical systems can be reconnected.

The factory-made system uses standard components in various configurations such as roof, wall panels and windows, internal and external cladding. This permits a rapid start when an order is placed.

There is no limitation on the size of EcoCanopy buildings. They can be as small as a single 4x4m canopy or as large as a school, in one or two storeys, anywhere that small, open-plan buildings are needed.

Timber forms all the main structural elements, including the distinctive roof module with its north-facing skylight. The roof cassette, made of timber beams with metal connectors, arrives on site completely prefabricated with integrated

building services. Walls follow a smaller grid in which windows and doors can be inserted.

EcoCanopy offers large internal spaces, with clear spans up to 8m (with a supplementary steel beam) and unlimited length. The typical internal height is 2.7m.

An independent assessment by the Waste & Resources Action Programme (WRAP) shows that 97% of materials supplied to EcoCanopy are actually used in the end product. (WRAP's comparable figure for conventional construction sites is 85%.) Of the 3% residue, 90% is recycled or reused; hence, material waste is less than 0.5%.

EcoCanopy uses C16 and C24 softwoods for the structure, with cedar cladding, all sourced from managed forests with Forest Stewardship Council Chain of Custody certification. Roof beam and wall-to-floor connections are by custom-designed steel brackets. All other connections are by screws and bolts.

The building can also integrate micro renewables such as PV panels, solar hot water panels, wind turbines and combined heat and power systems. EcoCanopy is naturally ventilated and uses carefully orientated roof lights that cut energy consumption.

SYSTEM SUPPLIER	A1M Timber Building Systems
STRUCTURAL ENGINEER	Gledsdale Associates

OVERVIEW

A1M has developed a relocatable timber system capable of building up to five storeys. The panelised system is transported on conventional lorries, and then assembled to its full volume on site. Benefits include rapid erection without scaffold, few vehicle movements, low floor-to-floor sound transmission and economical foundations.

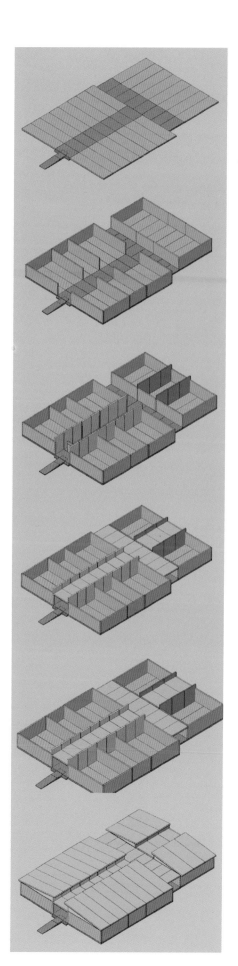

Architects will find the system adapts easily to many applications in education, healthcare, commercial, housing, light industrial and small office buildings. Currently the system is proposed for a new school that will be relocated eventually to a permanent location. In essence, this is a permanent structure with the ability to relocate.

Bolted connections enable the building to be disassembled in the opposite way to which it was assembled, with the speed of construction being similar to a volumetric approach.

The system exploits timber to avoid cold bridging and provide generous insulation. Typical insulated panel thickness is 200mm, giving a U-value down to 0.18. The system can be adapted to meet future changes to the Building Regulations.

In its single storey form, the panels lock together and provide lateral stability by diaphragm action. For higher structures, a slender steel skeleton carries all vertical loads to ground and resists lateral forces in moment connections. Infill panels can be timber framed or glazed.

The basic module is 3m x 9m (12m possible clear span) and floor-to-floor height can be up to 5m. The intermediate floor detail is particularly suitable for curtain walling applications.

The modular design permits circular buildings and curved structures to be generated from a common module. Service ducts are included in the system to accommodate mechanical and electrical services after the structure is erected. Under-floor heating comes built in to the floor cassettes.

All ply, OSB and CLS timbers are FSC or PEFC certified.

The Rapid Technology Transfer Group has provided the development forum to take the system from concept to market within a framework of deliver partners.

A1M
Modular system

The House That Kevin Built
Grand Designs, Channel 4, 2008

CLIENT	Grand Designs, Channel 4
ARCHITECTS	BBM Sustainable Design
STRUCTURAL ENGINEER	ModCell
TIMBER SUPPLIER	ModCell
CONTRACTOR	Eurban

OVERVIEW

ModCell is a timber panel system designed for use in residential, educational and commercial projects. With 2016 zero carbon housing in mind, it combines modern prefabrication with renewable straw bale infill and hemp cladding to make a truly sustainable solution. The building can be assembled quickly and efficiently, with thermal performance up to three times better than the current building regulations require.

Over a five day period in May 2008, ModCell helped to assemble 'The House That Kevin Built' at London's Excel Exhibition Centre for Channel 4's Grand Designs Live. It has ModCell Straw™ and ModCell Hemp™ panels on the ground floor, supporting a Facit timber system at first floor.

Although not deliberately designed for reuse, it was immediately apparent to Channel 4 that ModCell's system would pass a critical test: that the building is reused after the event. ModCell can be dismantled in the reverse order of assembly. After the recording and exhibition, the house would be taken apart and reassembled elsewhere as a demonstration.

Glue laminated FSC or PEFC certified European softwood, mostly spruce, is used for the frames. The components have engineered dovetail joints and the panels can be load-bearing up to three storeys. Manufactured using computerised numerical controlled cutting equipment, the frames are accurate to 2mm over a 10m length. This ensures rapid assembly to fine tolerances for good air tightness. The individual panels are bolted together, making it easy to dismantle.

ModCell's method of achieving low embodied energy is to assemble the frames in 'flying' factories. Instead of using a central fabrication plant and transporting the panels over great distances, they work with local farmers to identify a source of straw and a suitable location for assembly within a few miles of the construction site.

The structural timber frame is infilled using locally sourced straw bales; the panels are then plastered using a protective lime render, allowing them to 'breathe'. This ensures that the relative humidity level within the panel stays well below the level required for decomposition to occur. The lime also helps the panel to achieve a two-hour fire rating.

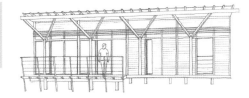

ARCHITECTS	Batterham Matthews Design
MANUFACTURER	Carpenter Oak and Woodland

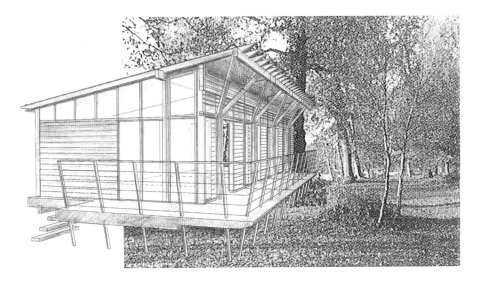

OVERVIEW

These modular woodland lodges, designed to use green (unseasoned) timber, compete head-on with the traditional demountable dwellings used in holiday parks. With integral deck and natural wood finish, the intention is to provide greater warmth and character, and more environmentally sustainable credentials than competitors.

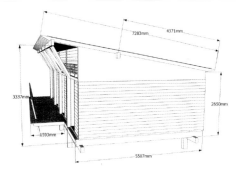

Woodland Lodges
Modular system

Holiday accommodation of this type is technically a caravan. Licence rules dictate that the structure must not be permanent and must be able to leave site in not more than two lorry loads. Furthermore, as a caravan may not be built on site, off-site fabrication is essential.

The basic module is 6.5m x 3m, with an optional 1.56m cantilevered deck. Two units can be transported on an articulated lorry. The serviced modules connect together and disassemble easily.

Two sections could be used for a single 'studio' unit, and four sections together would be suitable for a three-bedroom family unit. Subject to local regulations, multiple units could be connected for larger groups.

In keeping with suitability for purpose and sustainable supply of materials, the hybrid frame and panel system uses green timber in post and beam construction. (Engineered glue laminated timbers would be over specified.) The designers followed TRADA's *Green Oak in Construction* for the oak panels and Douglas fir frames. Hence, the

frame has an ultra low embodied energy level and is made entirely using materials from certified sustainable forests.

By mounting the structure on either timber piles or low impact steel screw foundations, the buildings can be installed with minimal disturbance of the ground. The roof is a timber deck with insulation and sedum roof covering. The integrated biomass boiler and solar water heating make these lodges close to 'zero carbon'.

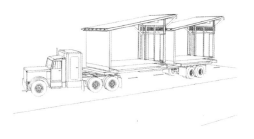

SYSTEM DESIGNER	AcerMetric
STRUCTURAL ENGINEER	AcerMetric with support from TRADA
CONTRACTORS	Nominated licensed contractors

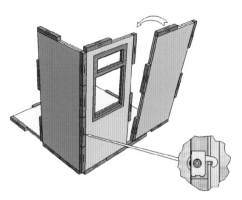

OVERVIEW

The secret to this timber building system is a patented 3D over-centre cam lock. The interlocking panels are adaptable to many small building purposes including housing, light industrial, sheds, small offices and emergency shelters. Rearrange the partitions for change of use. Need to grow vertically or horizontally? Just add more panels. And when no longer needed, take it apart for storage and reassembly.

Building services, including electrics and plumbing, are integrated within the system and push-fit together on site. With five prototypes in service, AcerMetric is now concentrating on interior and exterior cladding systems, which will integrate with the system, as well as a three-bedroom fully functional show house.

Designers can adapt the interlocking panels to most one, two and three-storey layouts in entirely timber construction. For higher structures, and where large spans are needed, AcerMetric reinforce the panels with a patented lightweight clamping beam and column system. There is no theoretical limit to the size, shape or style of buildings.

AcerMetric Modular system

The brief was for a system that could be factory made then assembled on site by unskilled labour. From concept to installation, the no-fuss-no-mess process is quick, clean and economical. And because it is substantially of timber construction, the CO_2 footprint is low.

Computer numerical control (CNC) converts traditional joinery and furniture techniques for accurate mass production of wall, floor and roof panels. The panels, made of C24 spruce, birch and ply, are then flat packed or sub-assembled into volumetric modules and transported to site where 'just one tool constructs it all'.

The speed of delivery is impressive. For example, AcerMetric estimate that a 250m² children's centre would need only 12 weeks from beginning of design to assembly of the structure. Response time for basic emergency accommodation can be compressed.

CLIENT	Willmott Dixon Re-Thinking
ARCHITECTS	White Design
STRUCTURAL ENGINEER AND TIMBER SUPPLIER	Eurban
CONTRACTOR	Willmott Dixon Construction

OVERVIEW

We teach children the need to be adaptable. Schools too must learn to adapt to demographic pushes and pulls. The Re-Thinking School is ready for the call, but its next life might not be as a school at all; designers are already planning for the school to morph into a medical centre.

Re-Thinking School
BRE Innovation Park, 2007

This mini school, on exhibition at BRE's Innovation Park, demonstrates ideas for sustainable materials. Built in solid wood panels (SWP) made from recycled off-cuts, it was designed to be relocated. The panels are butt jointed using 375mm screws. The R&D aspect of the project includes testing the method and ease of dismantling the structure.

The school aims to demonstrate that modern methods of construction can be materially sustainable, low carbon (both embodied and operational), cost effective and beautiful. The design uses natural ventilation and day lighting, adopts 'one planet living' methodology and can be used as an example when teaching children about sustainable living.

The 12m x 9m building at BRE has two and a half storeys. But the solid timber system could, in theory, go to 10 storeys. The timber structure was placed on a steel frame with screw piles, chosen so they could be removed and reused when the building is disassembled. The entire structure is manufactured in a factory and then brought to site for assembly.

The Re-Thinking School has been designed and engineered using cross-laminated solid wood panels to reduce its carbon footprint in construction and operation. These precisely cut timber wall, floor and roof elements enable the construction of airtight structures. Because of its tremendous ability to absorb heat, solid timber construction will reduce the risk of summer overheating and reliance on mechanical cooling systems, and retain warmth in the winter.

Post-completion tests demonstrate that solid timber structures, with easy details at panel junctions, deliver the required acoustic performance.

The Re-Thinking School supports sustainability as a core element of the curriculum. The school building itself becomes a teaching and learning tool; every part of the school's design, construction and operation is an educational opportunity.

CLIENT	Annika Eriksson
ARCHITECTS	Hopkins Architects
STRUCTURAL ENGINEER	Expedition Engineering
CONTRACTOR	ISG
SPECIALIST TIMBER CONTRACTOR	Wood-Newton

OVERVIEW

It is hard to imagine a reusable building less complicated than this enchanting mobile cinema. There is no taking apart and making good. Just charge the batteries, hitch it up and tow it to the next location.

The cinema exhibits work of the artist Annika Eriksson, one of Sweden's most widely exhibited artists, yet it is an exhibit in its own right.

Annika Eriksson has made a series of films set in Regents Park, paying tribute to public spaces that are free for everyone. The films will be shown in the tiny mobile cinema that will be towed to locations around the park during the London Festival of Architecture. Afterwards, the cinema will be used again in various indoor locations and may be relocated overseas.

The 5m x 2.3m mobile building is nearly 3.3m tall and seats six. It has a monocoque skeleton and skin structure over a 100mm thick base, all mounted on a steel flatbed trailer. A plywood external skin spans between rib elements fabricated from plywood sections with staggered butt joints. The denser build up of diminishing ribs and skins forms a portal frame at each end. Longitudinal stability is assured by diaphragm action. The ribs are anchored to longitudinal timber floor joists via bolted metal plates.

M&E is minimal, with basic lighting, projection power and floor-mounted fans to assist ventilation.

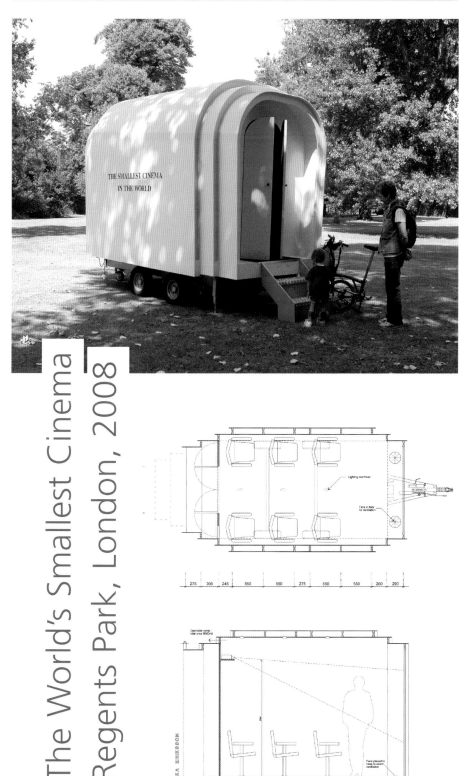

The World's Smallest Cinema
Regents Park, London, 2008

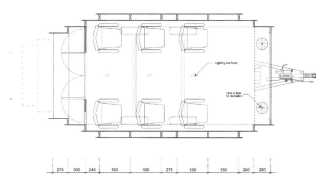

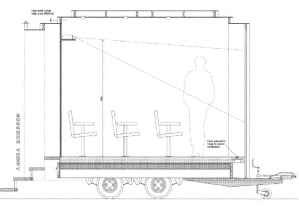

CLIENT	HFW Interactive
ARCHITECTS	Satellite Architects
STRUCTURAL ENGINEER	Elliott Wood Partnership
TIMBER SUPPLIER	The Timber Frame Company

OVERVIEW

This cleverly demountable structure is plywood clad when it shelters bus passengers during winter. Come springtime, it dons hemp cloth shading for its summer job as a travelling food stall. The timber components, selected from sustainable sources, can be packed flat for easy transport in a van.

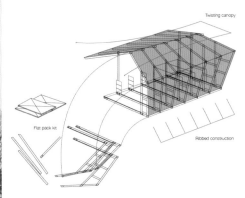

Wood connections are all M12 bolts, with the exception of the angle brackets that attach the beam at the front of the structure. Spacer tubing is used around 12mm rods in the ridge to keep uniform spacing between the ribs. Finally, a tension cable braces the back wall for lateral stability. The plywood floor is screwed to the floor joists that sit on used railway sleepers.

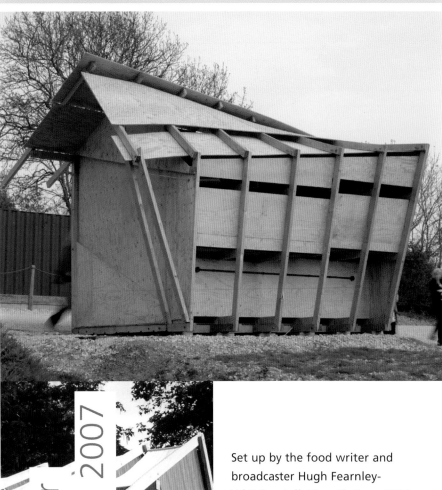

Food stall / bus shelter
River Cottage, Devon, 2007

Set up by the food writer and broadcaster Hugh Fearnley-Whittingstall, River Cottage HQ is a 60-acre organic farm nestled in the Axe Valley in East Devon. Satellite Architect's commission was to create a demountable food stall that River Cottage could take to outdoor food events throughout the country. The eye-catching design has proven fit for its dual purposes.

River Cottage insisted the food stall come with impeccable sustainability credentials and that it must have a secondary, off-season use. For the frame, Satellite chose Western red cedar because it would weather well and had FSC Chain of Custody certification. Similarly, they selected the hemp and plywood cladding from proven sustainable sources.

Frame magazine featured its first outing as a barbecue stand at the London Architecture Biennale in 2006 (now known as the London Festival of Architecture). And the stall was shortlisted for the Wood Awards and for the Architects' Journal Small Projects Award.

The 10m² stall stands 3.2m tall and can be erected by three people in under an hour.

Satellite Architects, together with the structural engineers from Elliott Wood, assembled the £10,000 prototype as a team-building exercise. While the rough-hewn finish sits well with River Cottage's style, production engineering would improve build quality and trim the unit cost.

CLIENT	HFW Interactive
ARCHITECTS	Satellite Architects
STRUCTURAL ENGINEER	Paul Carpenter Associates
TIMBER SUPPLIER	The Timber Frame Company

OVERVIEW
A construction sequence problem prompted this economical solution. Initial use as a toilet block will give way to a retail stall when permanent ablutions emerge from the main scheme at River Cottage Headquarters.

Toilet block
River Cottage, Devon, 2007

Satellite Architects' ability to produce quirky designs came to the fore in this toilet block. The concept responds to the existing buildings but then adds a modern twist through the ways the materials are used and the subtle twisting geometry.

River Cottage had its events space ready, but the building that would hold the toilets was not yet completed. They needed a solution for guests' toilets that would be eco-friendly, quick, inexpensive, built of sustainable materials and reusable. It also needed to be installed with minimum disruption to other construction activities on the site.

The solution was a temporary building in the courtyard that could be used as a WC until the other buildings were completed, and then relocated and converted into a fruit stall. It houses two WCs, one for disabled users, and is connected to a reed filtration system to treat the sewage.

The structure consists of pre-fabricated softwood frames, clad internally with cedar. External cladding is reclaimed corrugated steel sheets and Larix fresh sawn larch. With its natural oils, the larch will withstand the elements and weather to a silver colour. The bases are recycled oak railway sleepers. New timbers were from FSC certified UK forests.

The 7.8m x 3.1m stressed-skin structure uses portal action for transverse stability and diaphragm action longitudinally.

The structure, including external cladding, was built off-site and lowered into place. The cedar lining was added on site to allow for the plumbing, which was connected just in time for the first event.

Satellite has proposed a similar system of temporary WCs at the 2012 Olympics that could be reused as newsagents, bus stops and fruit stalls.

ARCHITECTS	Bryden Wood Associates
STRUCTURAL ENGINEER	Bryden Wood McLeod
CONTRACTOR	ICS
TIMBER SUPPLIER	Finnforest

OVERVIEW

The patented Rapid Deployment System (RDS) is an open-plan single-storey building that is easily transportable to virtually anywhere in the world. RDS buildings include services, glazing and finishes, and are ideal for temporary offices, retail, corporate entertainment or accommodation.

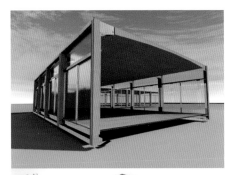

Rapid Deployment System
Modular system

To appreciate what 'rapid' means, think about how long it takes to assemble garden furniture. Once the modules are in position, two people can erect an RDS module in 30 minutes. The modules have self-levelling sole plates and joints simply 'zip' up (like the zip lock on a freezer bag). Side walls flip up into place; end walls flip up and unfold. Units without end walls have storage space for foldaway furniture. Any number of units can be zipped together. No crane is needed; units are lowered from a lorry onto skates, wheeled into place and then assembled with just one tool.

The 3.5m-wide modules can be up to 10m long. Although 3m high when assembled, the modules collapse to 650mm for efficient shipping, thus countering one of the arguments against pre-fabricated volumetric buildings. That is how a 140m² building, made up of five 8m-long RDS modules, can be transported on one lorry without special permission or escort.

Being a reusable and adaptable structure, it is inherently sustainable. Its thermal properties are closer to a permanent building than to a marquee or tent. In its basic form, RDS is intended as a temporary structure (for less than two years' use) and does not comply with part L2 of the Building Regulations. But it can be adapted for permanent occupation. Although ultraportable, RDS does not look temporary and offers the quality and rigidity of a permanent building. High-spec finishes include hardwood flooring, stainless steel, glass and adjustable lights. If desired, a water tank for thermal mass

can be built into the units.
The RDS uses timber components wherever possible for structural parts, as well as for cladding. Modules have a timber roof, with 90mm-thick Finnforest Kerto beams spanning 8-10m. The beam shape is optimised for structural performance and light weight, reducing to a mere 100mm depth at mid span. The roof beams and wall modules behave together as a portal frame.

The RDS features a patented steel mechanism that forms a stiff corner connection at roof level and doubles as a hinge to allow the structure to be collapsible. The 'intelligent' hinge mechanism is laser-cut from a single sheet of steel with the parts designed to be self-aligning to maintain dimensional tolerances. The hinge minimizes the weight and size of the collapsed modules and enables a safe erection process without the use of a crane. Walls and roof are instantly locked into upright position by hooks and their interface is automatically weathertight.

Its budget price makes RDS an attractive option for high-spec, open-plan demountable buildings.

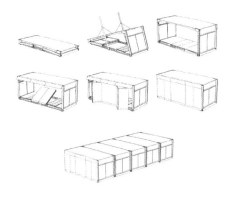

CLIENT	The Roman Catholic Diocese of East Anglia
ARCHITECTS	Gotch Saunders and Surridge
STRUCTURAL ENGINEER	Ramboll Whitbybird
CONTRACTOR	Kier Eastern
TIMBER SUPPLIER	KLH UK

OVERVIEW

The simple connections used in solid wood panel (SWP) structures make them potentially demountable. The panels are half lapped at all intersection edges and then fastened together with long steel screws. The structure would disassemble in reverse order.

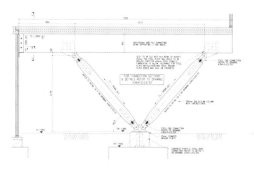

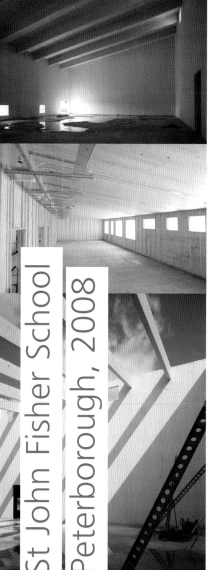

St John Fisher School
Peterborough, 2008

Rapid construction, sleek lines and low carbon footprint made SWP (also known as cross-laminated timber panels) the logical choice for this school redevelopment. The wall, floor and roof panels – pre-cut with half-lap joints and openings for doors and windows – were transported to site disassembled and then erected with few temporary supports. The 3D diaphragm structure is immensely strong and stable.

Glulam beams were fitted into pockets in the wall panels and then fixed with steel angles. Zed sections connected floor panels in areas of extremely long span floors. The glulam column assemblies were test-assembled in the factory and then disassembled to be shipped to site. Once on site they were reassembled with ease – and could be easily disassembled in future.

In keeping with the Diocese's aspirations for social, economic and environmental sustainability, the new buildings came with an attractive construction cost and short duration on site. And the timber solution is a net absorber of carbon, even allowing for fabrication and transport; an equivalent steel and concrete building would carry a significant embodied energy penalty.

The thickest panels used on the project were 230mm and the largest panels were approximately 11.7m x 2.4m. The cross-laminated panels were formed from spruce strips, nominally graded C24. The glulam beams and columns were grade GL28h spruce.

The two-storey classroom block (60m x 17m x 9.2m high) was an obvious candidate for timber panels. A traditional solution to the large classrooms, voided central corridors and open spaces would have been structurally complex. The final cellular layout is composed of load bearing timber panel walls, floors and roofs.

The sports hall (18m x 34m x 11.7m high), originally intended to have a glulam beam and column frame, was switched to cross-laminated panel construction because the frame would have projected too far and required an unacceptable stepped façade. The sports hall and drama studio form a rigid box structure that is robust, very quickly erected and architecturally pleasing.

Cross-laminated deep beams were used to support roof panels. No roof purlins were required; the aluminium cladding was simply fastened to the KLH roof panels via top hat supports.

Wood for reusable structures

Wood is processed into many products, each with distinctive mechanical and aesthetic properties.
Here we review the common types and highlight their applications in reusable structures.

Description	Applications	Case studies

Softwood (coniferous trees)

Description	Applications	Case studies
For reusable buildings, softwood's advantages include good strength to weight, lightness and easy workability. For internal use, untreated non-durable softwoods are extensively used, e.g. European redwood (pine), European whitewood (spruce). For external use, or in areas of high humidity, non-durable species should be pressure/vacuum treated with preservative. The preservative loading will depend on the particular application. For structural use, the wood should be either visually or machine graded and kiln dried to 20% or less to reduce shrinkage in use.  Some softwood species are sufficiently durable to use externally for certain applications without treatment provided that sapwood is excluded e.g. Western red cedar (durable), imported Douglas fir or European larch (moderately durable). All softwoods, whether homegrown or imported, are available from certified sources.	Internal joinery Panelling Staircases Balustrades Screens Roof trusses Rafters Joists Framing Cladding External joinery Structural members Decking Louvres Beams	EcoCanopy Buckingham Palace Ticket Office Monkey Puzzle Pavilion Terrace Restaurant A1M system AcerMetric system Woodland lodges Foodstall and bus stop Toilet block

Hardwood (deciduous trees)

Description	Applications	Case studies
Hardwood may not be first choice for reusable buildings because of weight and cost. Although hardwood is available from both temperate and tropical sources, it is very unlikely that tropical woods would be used in reusable buildings in the UK. The long-term durability and strength may be unnecessary, and the additional weight is probably a disadvantage. Temperate hardwoods such as ash, beech, birch, sycamore, walnut, white oak and cherry can be used internally, but are relatively expensive. For external use, European oak and sweet chestnut are the only temperate hardwoods considered durable, but sapwood must be excluded.	Flooring Decking Structure External Cladding Panelling External joinery	Terrace Restaurant (sub-structure) Woodland lodges

Description	Applications	Case studies

Hardwood (deciduous trees) continued

For structural use, these woods need to be visually stress graded. If used green (undried), make allowance for possible distortion and shrinkage after installation.[10]

Structural frames in oak are often used with traditional carpentry joints. These may not be easy to dismantle when part of a reusable building.

Both oak and sweet chestnut will exude tannin for some time, particularly if the wood is used 'green'. This can lead to corrosion of exposed mild steel, and staining of other materials, unless protected during the weathering period. Stainless steel is recommended for fixings.

The majority of temperate hardwoods can be obtained from certified sources, whether homegrown or imported. A limited number of tropical hardwoods is available from certified sources.

Laminated veneer lumber (LVL)

LVL is manufactured from rotary peeled veneers glued together to form continuous panels, rather like plywood.

One type has the grain of the wood in all the veneers running parallel to each other, producing material for joists and beams. The other type has some veneers placed with the grain at right angles to the other layers. This produces a product with more uniform stiffness, better suited to more specialised engineering uses like shear diaphragms and panels.

Applications: LVL is good for long spans, and is ideal for roof and floor joist and lintels/framework studs, both in new build and renovation, where strength is needed.

LVL is manufactured in 1.8m wide panels and can be cut to beam sizes with widths from 20mm - 600mm, thicknesses from 27mm - 75mm to a maximum length of 26m.

Case studies: Westminster ticket office

Serpentine Gallery

Swoosh

Modcell

Glulam

Glulam is made from layers of parallel solid timber laminates (normally spruce or pine but occasionally larch or even hardwoods such as oak). The laminates are glued together under high pressure into large structural sections that are free of knots, flaws, splits, etc. The weather resistant glue can be specified either dark or light. Fire safety is similar to solid timber; slow to char, the uncharred section of the beam retains its strength.

Applications: Glulam often catches the eye of designers for use in specialist buildings. However, glulam can be used for most load-bearing structures where visual appearance is important.

It is generally available in standard widths of 90mm - 240mm, and lengths of up to 12m. Other sizes may be available to order.

Glulam can be made in a wide variety of forms, from straight beams to rounded columns, roof trusses to complex pyramid shapes, and from simple curved beams to large domes and arches.

Case studies: Globe at CERN

St John Fisher School

Description	Applications	Case studies

Solid wood panels (SWP)

These are cross-laminated sections of kiln-dried spruce. SWP buildings have a very low carbon footprint because the material itself is an excellent insulator and it locks away the carbon absorbed during growth.

Wall, floor and roof elements can be pre-cut in the factory to any dimension and shape, including openings for doors, windows, stairs etc. SWP structures can offer high thermal, acoustic and fire performance to meet Building Regulation requirements.

These large solid panels form walls, roofs, floors and even lift shafts and stairs. The building envelope can be easily clad with other materials such as timber, brick, mineral render, or composite panels.

Standard panel dimensions range from 51mm up to 300mm in thickness, while larger panels as thick as 500mm can also be produced.

Panel length and width dimensions are mostly limited by what can be transported to site and can be up to 4.8m wide and 15m long.

Westminster ticket office

Deutscher Pavilions

St John Fisher School

Re-Thinking School

I-joists

Timber I-joists consist of timber flanges (typically solid timber or LVL) and a panel product web (usually OSB). Metal-web timber joists combine timber flanges with metal strutting webs.

Timber I-beams have proved to be a cost-effective solution for floor and roof construction because of their lightweight, long length (allowing large spans) and dimensional stability.

Monkey Puzzle Pavilion

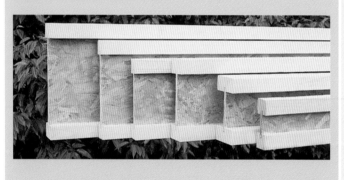

Oriented strand board (OSB)

OSB consists of resin-bonded sheets made up of small, thin strands of wood, compressed into layers to form a mat. It has good dimensional stability and no knots or voids in the structure.

OSB has good strength properties and is low cost.

Different grades and thicknesses suit each use depending on the strength required for the particular structural application.

Monkey Puzzle Pavilion

A1M system

Description	Applications	Case studies

Medium density fibreboard (MDF)

MDF is an engineered, stiff, flat sheet that is knot-free and made from wood fibres. MDF is sometimes colour coded by dyes in the board layers to indicate its use:

Green – for moisture resistant
Grey – for exterior use
Red – sheets with flame retardant chemicals.

MDF has no surface grain and can be machined, drilled, cut and filled easily without damaging the surface. MDF is also available in finished product e.g. skirtings, architraves and other mouldings.

Fire rated and external grades are available.

Plywood

Plywood is a versatile sheet material. Softwood plywood is usually made from European grown spruce or pine, whilst birch is a common hardwood plywood.

Imported plywoods may be of various hardwood species (but not all necessarily durable) and softwoods such as Douglas fir.

Spruce is less decorative than birch and is used where a visual appearance is not so important. Birch plywood can have a clearer, knot-free appearance, depending on the grade selected. Both plywoods have grades related to their appearance.

World's Smallest Cinema

Buckingham Palace Ticket Office

A1M system

AcerMetric system

Foodstall and bus stop

Modified wood

Softwoods can be modified to improve their performance. The advantage of modified wood is that low cost and plentiful species can be used, and the process results in higher moisture resistance. Acetylated wood, sold under the Accoya brand, treats sustainable wood species with acetic acid in a heat and pressure process that modifies the chemical structure. Heat treated wood, sold under the Thermowood name, uses heat to modify the wood's cellular structure.

External applications such as windows, doors, conservatories and cladding.

Westminister ticket office

Designing for reuse

Here are some principles to establish in the first design to ensure the structure can be adapted or disassembled for reuse.

Modular planning	Planning based on modular dimensions is more likely to make a structure reusable or adaptable for change of use.
	Horizontally, the layout must take account of panel or component sizes for practicality and economy.
	Vertically, take into account module heights and provision for floor and ceiling cassette systems.
	The layout should enable M&E services to be distributed with minimal penetrations of the structure.
Panelisation and connections	Panel dimensions will depend on overall size, stock material dimensions and ease of handling and installation.
	As a general rule, a structure designed for factory production is likely to be adaptable for reuse. This is because construction will consist of modules intended to be connected together on site. Provided the connections are accessible without destroying the cladding and finishes, the modules will be ready for disassembly in reverse order. In some cases internal linings on ceilings are designed to be sacrificed if the building is to be dismantled.
	Connections will usually be bolts, screws or wood pins. Ensure metal parts are corrosion resistant; otherwise, 'easy' dismantling may become 'difficult'.
	Avoid traditional carpentry joints (especially if glued) although these might be suitable if they are designed to be disassembled.
Cladding, finishes and fixings	Cladding should respect the panelisation. Therefore cladding and lining panels that match structural panels will be more reusable than (say) extensive plasterboard. Avoiding wet trades will generally enhance the reusability. Use screws instead of nails to attach cladding and lining.
	Cladding systems that 'bolt on' to the structure are eminently reusable.
	Where cladding, or lining, is intended to be removed before dismantling the structure, corrosion resistant screws will make this process easier. Hidden fixings in cladding board systems will make it easier to reuse the cladding because any imperfections in the fixings will be concealed in the rebuild.
	Brittle finishes will not survive reconstruction. So either avoid or plan for resurfacing. Painted systems are unlikely to be problematic because redecoration is likely in any case.

Foundations	Systems that impose minimal disturbance on the ground are preferred. Therefore, avoid integral concrete foundation and slab systems in favour of suspended floor cassette systems supported on an array of piles. Preferably, use mini piles that can be extracted or 'unscrewed'.
Building services	Service ducts are preferred in order to minimize penetrations of the structure and linings. Avoid concealing service runs in walls, floors and ceiling unless readily accessible.
Durability and robustness	Normally we think in terms of one installation process. For a reusable structure, designers must think through the dismantling, transport and re-erection processes. Reusability will be enhanced by selecting durable materials. Avoid features, such as projections, that could be easily damaged in dismantling and reconstruction.
Lifting points and scaffolding	Provide for lifting points in the original design and ensure they are permanent and remain accessible for dismantling. Systems that minimize scaffolding are more likely to be suitable for reuse. Try to make each floor a working platform for the next level.
Safety during dismantling	The designer's responsibility under the CDM Regulations includes ensuring the structure can be safely erected and demolished. Erection or dismantling should preferably not require scaffolding to meet CDM Regulations. Take care to ensure the structure can be kept stable while it is being dismantled or adapted for reuse.

References

[1] Food and Agriculture Organization of the United Nations, *State of the World's Forests*, 2007, Rome

[2] International Institute for Environment and Development, *Using wood products to mitigate climate change: a review of evidence and key issues for sustainable development*, 2004

[3] Department for Business Enterprise & Regulatory Reform, *The Code for Sustainable Homes*, 2006

[4] PEFC: Programme for the Endorsement of Forest Certification
FSC: Forest Stewardship Council

[5] TRADA, *Energy Efficient Housing – A Timber Frame Approach*, 1989

[6] European Commission, *EU Landfill Directive*, 1999

[7] Energy for Sustainable Development, *Carbon Calculator*

[8] Marsh, R. *The Energy of Building*, The Structural Engineer/Volume 67/No.24/19 December, 1989

[9] National Green Specification, *Green Spec*, 2008

[10] Ross, P., Mettem, C. and Holloway, A., TRADA Technology, *Green Oak in Construction*, 2007

Image credits

COVER
Top left: Groupe-H
Top right: Tim Soar, Hopkins Architects
Bottom right: Ioana Marinescu
Bottom left: Architectural Academy

INTRODUCTION
"Silver hut" TRADA archives

WESTMINSTER TICKET OFFICE
Morley von Sternberg

BAD DÜRRHEIM
Universität München

REUSABLE WOOD STRUCTURES
Top: Hopkins Architects
Middle: Morley von Sternberg
Bottom: Paul O'Neill, Bryden Wood

BUCKINGHAM PALACE TICKET OFFICE
All photographs: Tim Soar, Hopkins Architects
Drawing: Hopkins Architects

THE GLOBE AT CERN
Groupe-H

WESTMINSTER TICKET OFFICE
All images: Morley von Sternberg

MONKEY PUZZLE PAVILION
All images: Ioana Marinescu

SERPENTINE GALLERY
All images: Arup

DEUTSCHER PAVILIONS
All images: Finnforest

TERRACE RESTURANT
Main picture: George Wright
Right: George Wright
Bottom left: Cameron Scott

SWOOSH
All images: Architectural Academy

ECOCANOPY
All images: Bryden Wood Associates

A1M MODULAR SYSTEM
All images: A1M

MODCELL
All Images: Modcell

WOODLAND LODGES
All images: Carpenter Oak & Woodland

ACERMETRIC
All images: Acermetric

ST JOHN FISHER SCHOOL
All images: Cahit Okten

RE-THINKING SCHOOL
All images: Re-thinking

THE WORLD'S SMALLEST CINEMA
All drawings and images: Hopkins Architects

FOOD STALL / BUS SHELTER
All images: Satellite Architects

TOILET BLOCK
All images: Satellite Architects

RAPID DEPLOYMENT SYSTEM
All images: Bryden Wood Associates